W9-CBN-277

Graphic Organizers

...helping children think visually

Written by Kris Flynn
Edited by Barbara Maio

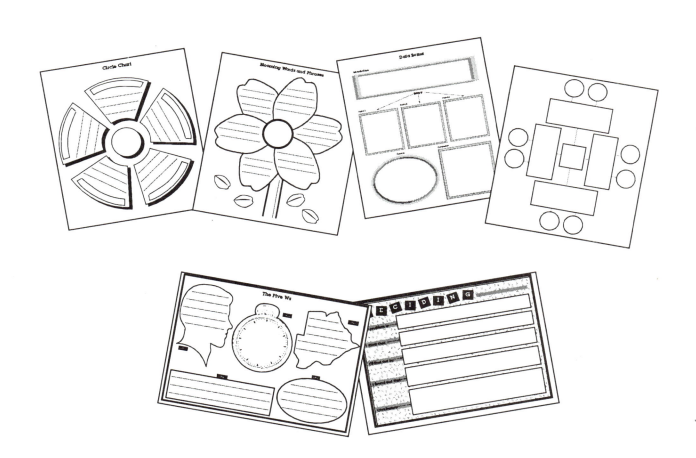

CTP ©1995, Creative Teaching Press, Inc., Cypress, CA 90630

Table of Contents

Introduction

In today's classrooms, students must read, comprehend, and remember information from a wide variety of texts. Most students need to visually process information and Graphic Organizers are powerful tools that help them accomplish this.

Graphic Organizers are visual representations of a student's knowledge of concepts and topics. They provide a frame for teachers and students to visually identify important facts, organize information, and record relationships between facts and ideas.

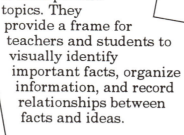

Graphic Organizers help students:

- understand how pieces of information are related.

- increase their comprehension and recall.

- organize their observations, research, opinions, and reflections.

- prepare written assignments and presentations.

- problem solve and integrate their thinking, reading, and writing processes.

- practice higher level thinking skills and apply the skills to real-world situations.

Graphic Organizers help teachers:

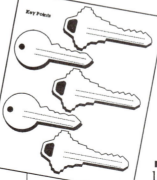

- explain and illustrate abstract concepts.

- focus students' attention on one part of the text while guiding them to see the overall sequence and interrelationships of the parts.

- provide second language learners with a visual image for new vocabulary and concepts.

- assist students with advance information and structure.

- review materials as a post-reading activity.

- evaluate student progress.

Using the Graphic Organizers:

Distribute individual copies or display on the overhead for group practice. *Note: Teacher modeling and classroom discussion are essential.*

Choose a common activity and model each step.

Brainstorm ideas and write them on the organizer.

Help students analyze their responses. Point out the relationships between facts and encourage students to connect ideas and information.

Sequencing

PURPOSE The events of life and literature often move in an ordered pattern. Asking students to order these events helps them recall what they learn.

WHAT TO DO Students, working individually, in partners or in groups, list each major event in a space on the Train Track. Looking at the track, students can retell or rewrite the information.

Literature

Some stories, like *I Know an Old Lady* by Wescott, are organized so a new part is added with each retelling. Students can review vocabulary and events by writing or drawing the new part each time they orally retell the story.

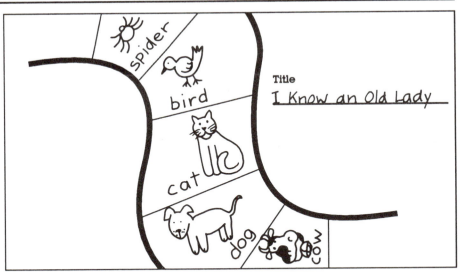

Music

Write or draw each part of the song on an index card or sticky note and distribute these to the students. As they sing the song, students add their part to the Train Track sequence at the correct time.

General Classroom Use

When a classroom activity involves learning new steps, use the Train Track to sequence the order of events. For example, when students prepare a report for the first time, they list the steps and add to the list as they discover another step.

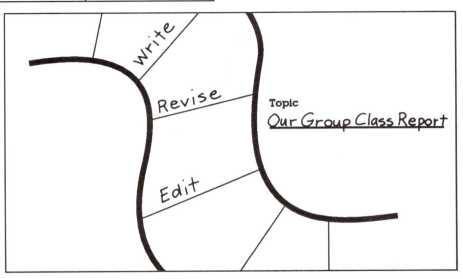

Name _____   Title _____

Train Track

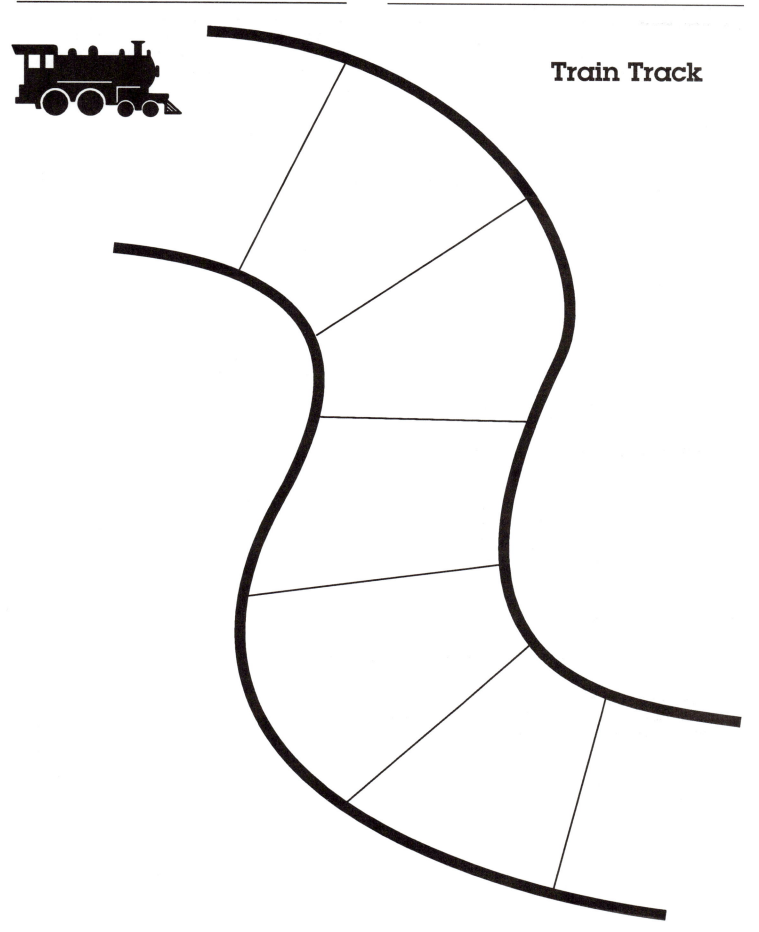

Sequencing

PURPOSE Use this chart with stories in which the sequence of events start and end in the same place. This chart helps students understand the structure and chain of events in a story.

WHAT TO DO Students determine how many events need to be sequenced around the circle. Then they decide how to divide the circle by the number of events. (This requires some mathematical practice.) Encourage students to use words or pictures to depict each event.

Literature
Students love to retell stories that begin and end in the same place—for example, *If You Give a Mouse a Cookie* by Numeroff. They can sequence these circular stories using pictures or words—or a combination of both.

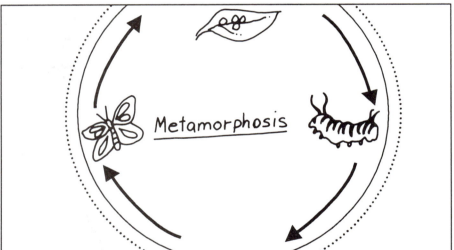

Science
Students use the chart to sequence the life cycle of plants or animals. They discover special relationships as they determine where to place their information on the circle. To reinforce the sequence, encourage students to add pictures cut from magazines.

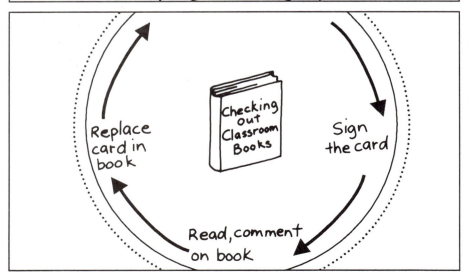

General Classroom Use
Record the sequence for classroom routines like checking out class library books. Then use the chart to show students the entire procedure—from taking books off the shelf to replacing them when they are returned.

Creative Teaching Press

Name _____   **Title/Topic** _____

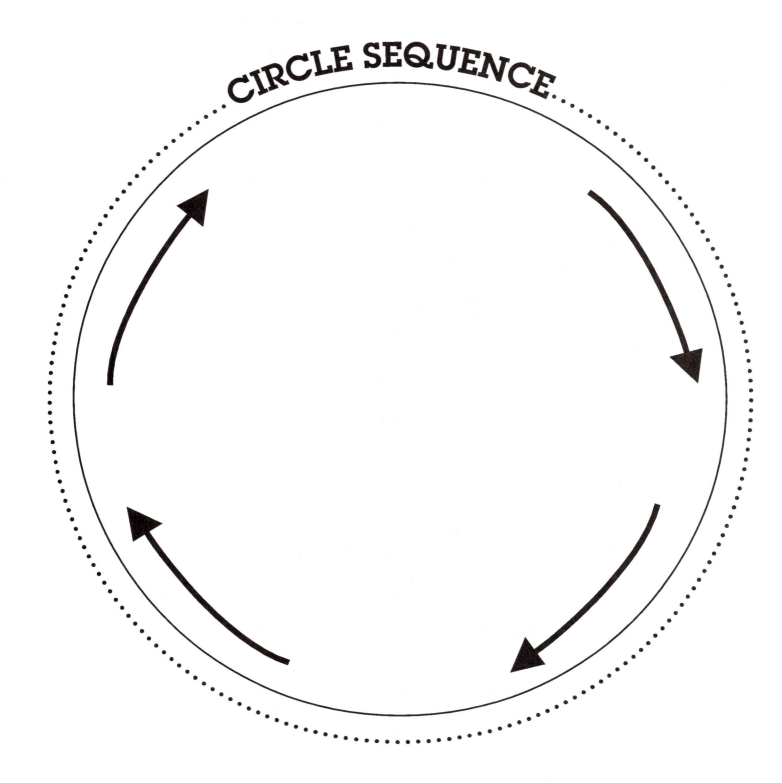

Sequencing

PURPOSE The Story Board is designed to help students identify main ideas and concepts and sequence events in logical order. Use this chart in all curriculum areas.

WHAT TO DO Students use words, pictures, or a combination of both to record a sequence of events. When they first sequence tasks, students should work with only three sections—the beginning, the middle, and the end.

 Literature
Use this chart with a book like *Jack and the Beanstalk* by Cauley or a selection from a reading text. Discuss with students that all stories have a beginning, middle, and end. Ask them to identify the beginning and the end—then they can accurately identify the middle section.

Social Studies
Sequencing a government or historical process helps students retain the information and clarify the order of events. Working in groups or individually, students choose the details they need.

Introduced in House or Senate	Goes into a committee or Sub-committee	Goes to Rules Committee

Title How a Bill Becomes Law

Goes to floor of House or Senate	Both Houses Vote	Goes to president for possible veto

Read recipe.	Gather ingredients, measuring tools, utensils.	Measure and mix.
Preheat oven. Grease pan.	Pour mix into pan. Bake and cool.	Frost and serve.

 **General Classroom Use**
Students can use the Story Board to sequence news articles or the events of their school day. They can also take notes or retell a story or classroom event. For example, when students cook in class, they record the sequence of directions on the Story Board.

Name _____

Title _____

Story Board

Brainstorming

PURPOSE Brainstorming words related to a topic helps students use the right side of their brain to organize their thoughts. Then, through discussion—class discussion is crucial—students begin to understand the meaning and use of words and their relationships.

WHAT TO DO Model the procedure with the class by selecting a word or topic for the center circle. Ask students to brainstorm related words, then group them. Write category names in the clouds. Each cluster becomes a main idea and details for a paragraph.

 **Literature**

Have students cluster events or special words from a story they enjoy. This activity encourages students to expand their vocabulary and enhance their written description of events.

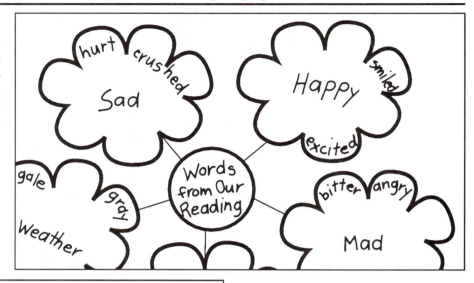

 Science or Social Studies

As a class, chose a topic for the cluster center—for example, pollution. Then ask students for related categories or sub-topics for the surrounding clouds. (Around each cloud students write the words related to each sub-topic.)

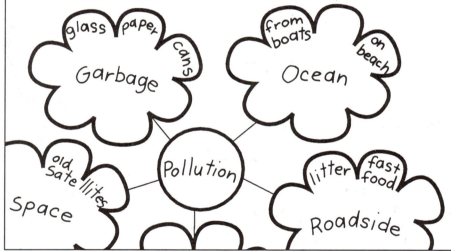

General Classroom Use

Clustering helps students problem solve in different school situations. For example, children are often frustrated by what they perceive as the restrictions of playground rules. Give them the opportunity to brainstorm reasons for these rules and to use this organizer to help clarify their thinking.

Brainstorming

PURPOSE Students use this organizer to sort information into more advanced and complex clusters. This chart allows students to record more detailed and elaborate information.

WHAT TO DO After students have successfully used Simple Clusters, introduce the idea of a main topic and several sub-topics with supporting details. Brainstorm the sub-topics and write these in the rectangles. Each sub-topic is supported by at least two details.

Literature
Have students cluster information about a story character or about the story itself. For example, in *The Twenty-One Balloons*, students collect information about the unusual life on the island of Krakatoa.

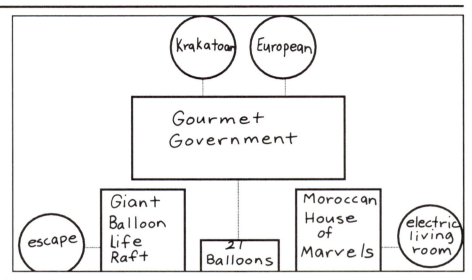

Social Studies
After viewing a film, students use the clusters to record the information they learn or to respond to specific questions about the topic. For example: they might answer the questions: "What makes the Grand Canyon so colorful? How would you describe its size?"

General Classroom Use
Show students how to organize their topic information so that each cluster group transfers directly into a paragraph.

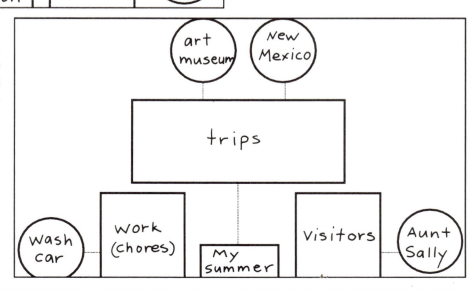

Complex Clusters

Classifying

PURPOSE Recording data in an easily understood visual pattern helps students organize information. When students work with Sorting Circles, they should first identify their sorting categories and then record their collected data.

WHAT TO DO In the center circle students write or draw their main topic. They should determine the categories for the outer circles. Remind students that they need not use every circle and they may want to add category circles.

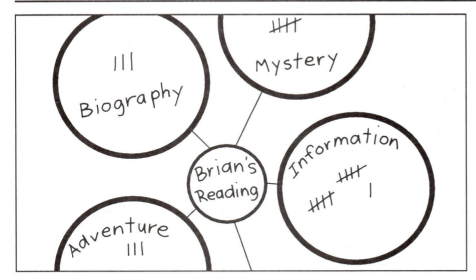

Literature

Have students use the organizer to evaluate and classify the books they read. Encourage students to examine the book classifications and then try to broaden their literature genre choices.

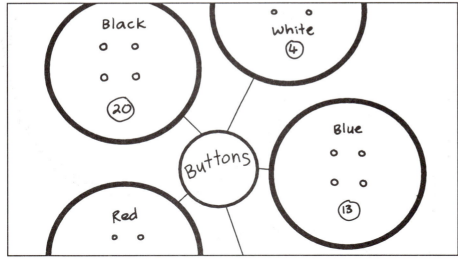

✖ Math

In the center circle students write the name of the objects to be sorted. Encourage cooperative work by asking student groups to determine their own sorting categories for the outer circles. For example, they may group buttons by shape or by the number of holes.

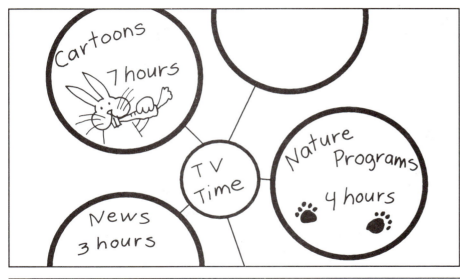

✎ General Classroom Use

Have students use the Sorting Circles to track the type of television programs they watch—sitcoms, game shows, news, nature programs. Then they use this data to help them make choices about their TV watching.

Sorting Circles

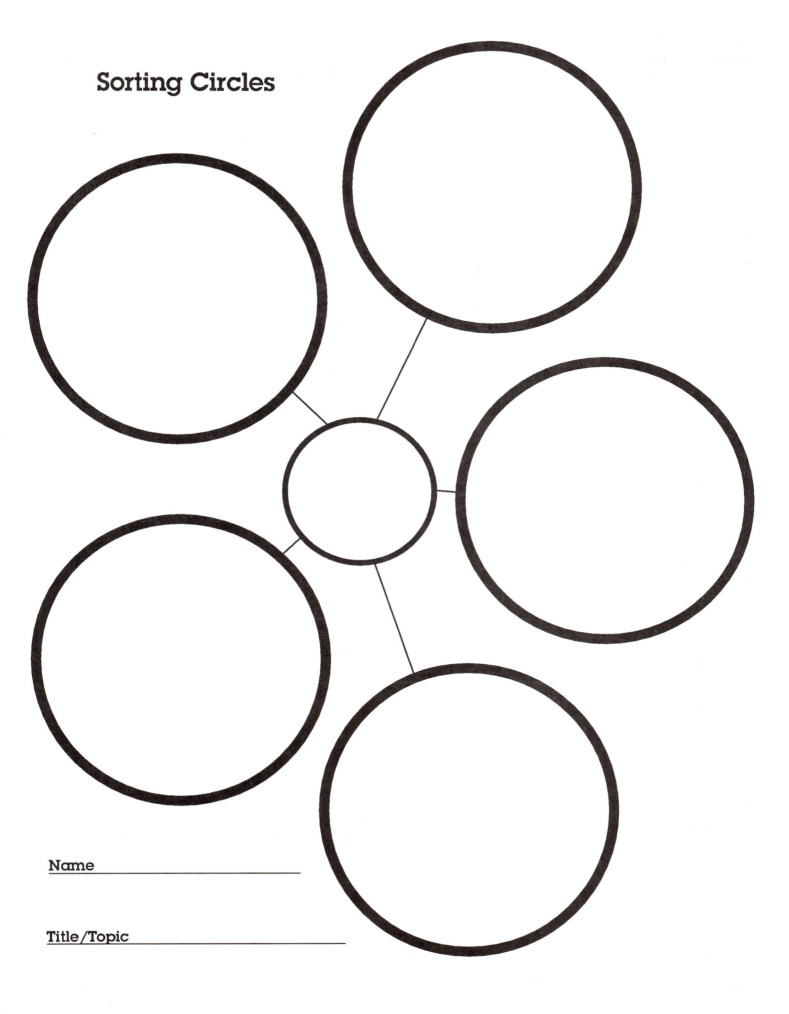

Name _____

Title/Topic _____

Classifying

PURPOSE By depicting informational categories as the segments of a circle, students begin to tie the information together as parts of a whole rather than isolated facts.

WHAT TO DO Use this chart to record information within the portions of a circle. Work with students to assign a different category or classification to each segment. In the center they write or draw a picture for the title. Students can use pictures cut from magazines to create a collage for the category.

Literature

Students use this chart to help identify story themes—thus broadening their understanding of the complexity of writing. For example, after reading *Annie and the Old One* by Miles, students write an important theme in each circle segment. They may also use the Circle Chart to evaluate and classify elements in their own writing. This encourages young authors to include more depth and detail.

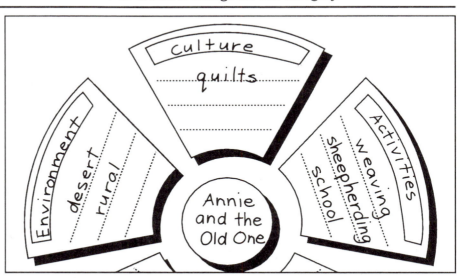

Science

Have students use the chart to organize their science research. As a research and decision-making activity, ask students to first determine the classification categories they will use.

General Classroom Use

During or after a field trip, students use the circle segments to record what they observe. For example, they write the names of animals and plants seen at the zoo. Filling in the chart helps students see that a "zoo" is really composed of a number of different parts.

Circle Chart

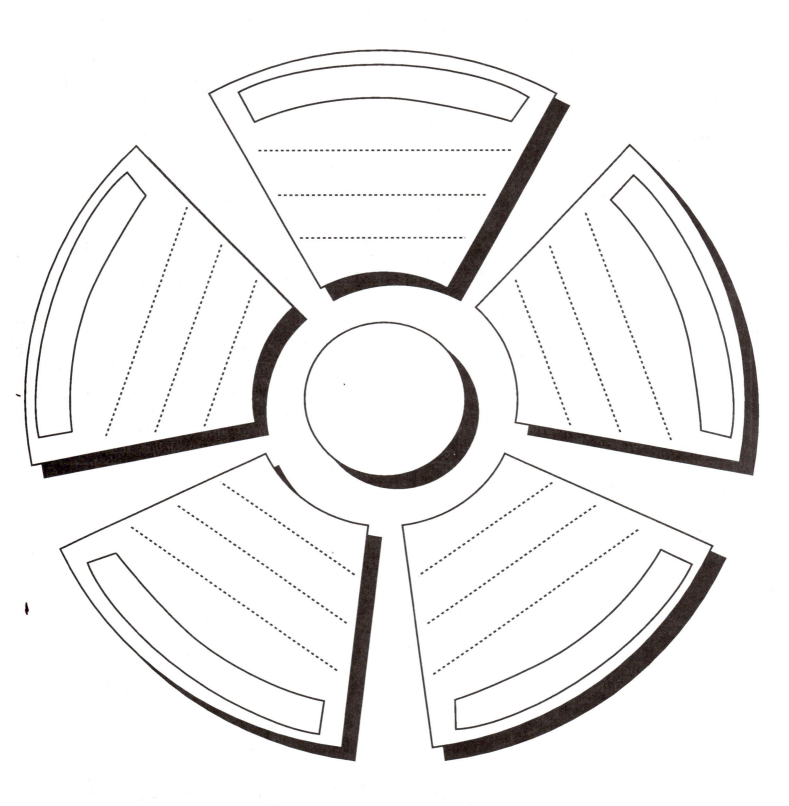

Classifying

PURPOSE Students use this chart to classify information by categories—a practical skill for many learning areas. As they classify, students compare information and make connections to what they already know. This chart helps them visually organize the information for future use.

WHAT TO DO Have students list general categories across the top of the chart. In the left column, students list specific items or the type of information they want to chart.

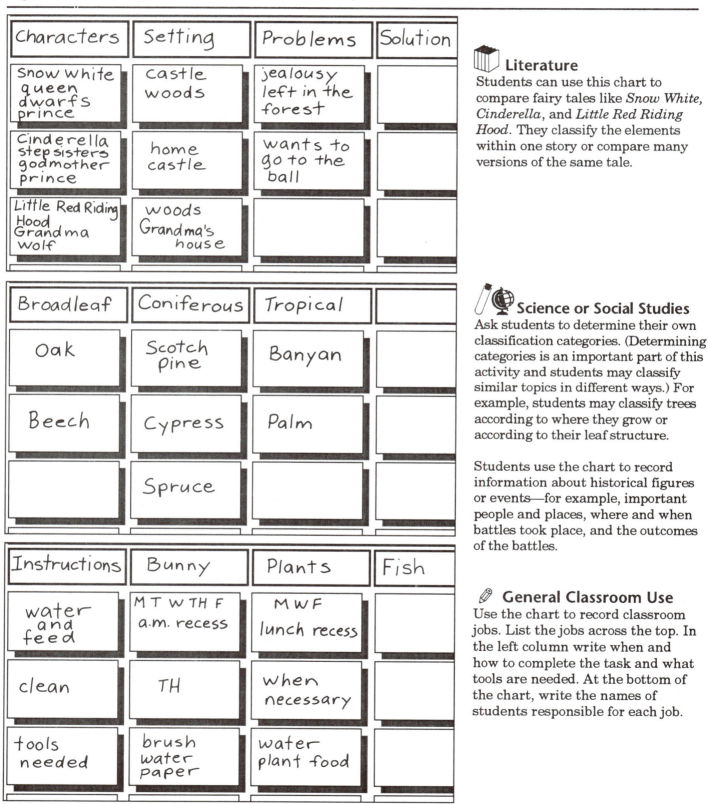

Characters	Setting	Problems	Solution
Snow white queen dwarfs prince	castle woods	jealousy left in the forest	
Cinderella step sisters godmother prince	home castle	wants to go to the ball	
Little Red Riding Hood Grandma wolf	woods Grandma's house		

Broadleaf	Coniferous	Tropical	
Oak	Scotch Pine	Banyan	
Beech	Cypress	Palm	
	Spruce		

Instructions	Bunny	Plants	Fish
water and feed	M T W TH F a.m. recess	M W F lunch recess	
clean	TH	when necessary	
tools needed	brush water paper	water plant food	

Literature
Students can use this chart to compare fairy tales like *Snow White*, *Cinderella*, and *Little Red Riding Hood*. They classify the elements within one story or compare many versions of the same tale.

Science or Social Studies
Ask students to determine their own classification categories. (Determining categories is an important part of this activity and students may classify similar topics in different ways.) For example, students may classify trees according to where they grow or according to their leaf structure.

Students use the chart to record information about historical figures or events—for example, important people and places, where and when battles took place, and the outcomes of the battles.

General Classroom Use
Use the chart to record classroom jobs. List the jobs across the top. In the left column write when and how to complete the task and what tools are needed. At the bottom of the chart, write the names of students responsible for each job.

Name

Title/Topic

Classifying Chart

Identifying

PURPOSE It is often difficult for students to identify the key points in a text. This graphic organizer uses pictures of keys to remind students of this task and to help them identify the main points in their reading.

WHAT TO DO After an event or unit study, ask students to identify the main points and write each one inside a key. It is important to model and practice this activity with the class before asking students to do it. Later, students can cut out the keys and sequence them to retell the events.

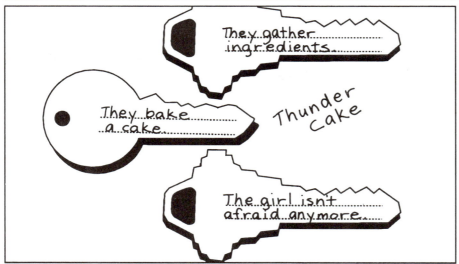

 Literature
After students read a book like *Thunder Cake* by Polacco, have them write the main (key) events of the story. It is helpful for students to work with a partner or small group to reach a consensus before writing the information.

 **Social Studies**
While reading a textbook, have students identify the key information from one section at a time. (The smaller the text selection, the more detailed the key parts.) As students grow more skilled, they can work with larger selections of text.

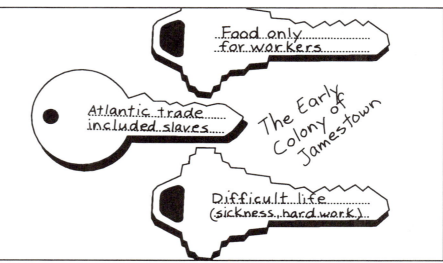

General Classroom Use
Have students record the important points of a current news event or class activity.

Key Points

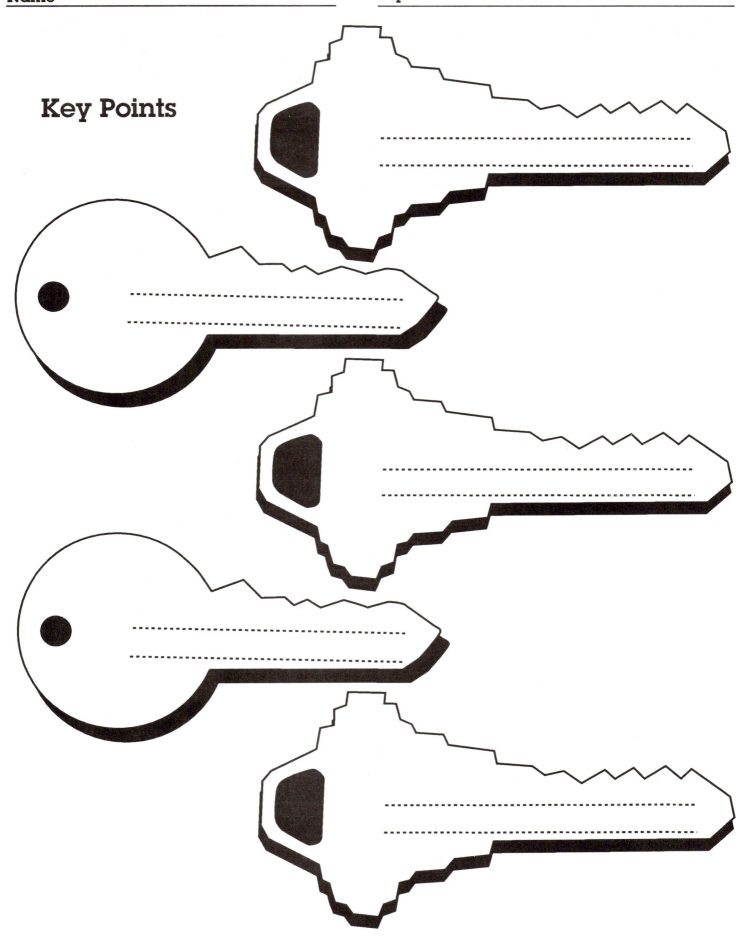

Identifying

PURPOSE Throughout their lives, students encounter problems and need to seek solutions. This graphic organizer helps students formulate several solutions to an identified problem.

WHAT TO DO On the left side students write the problem(s). They work in pairs or small groups to brainstorm solutions and write these on the right. They may want to discuss and/or implement some solutions and report on what worked best.

📖 Literature
Students identify and list the problems encountered by a story character like *Miss Rumphius* by Cooney. They look for the solutions in the story and evaluate them. Encourage students to suggest new solutions to the character's problems.

Problem	Solution
Miss R. wanted to make the world a more beautiful place.	She planted lupines. <hr> she also could have: – painted houses – picked weeds – picked up trash

Problem	Solution
Wars	
Democracy was threatened in Vietnam	Troops sent in Other possibilities: ① ②
People starving in Somalia	Send troops to distribute food

🌐 Social Studies
Have students identify the problems and solutions in a current event. For example, they bring in a newspaper article or take notes during a news report. They discuss and share their information, identifying the problem and solution being considered.

When looking at historical events, encourage students to discuss the solutions proposed at the time, then evaluate them by today's standards.

✏️ General Classroom Use
Classroom problems become learning experiences when students participate in the problem-solving process. Post the problems and solutions so parents become aware of the students' efforts to deal with difficult situations.

Problem	Solution
Paint in art area dries up	1. Put lids on 2. Check daily
Bunny cage smells	1. Clean more often 2. One table/week cleans cage
Graffiti on school building	

Problem

Solution

Identifying

PURPOSE Identifying the cause and effect of story events helps students see the consequences of a character's actions. By recognizing the causes and listing their effects, students learn to look at alternative choices that help in their own life decisions.

WHAT TO DO Students identify and write a cause on the left side and its effect (or effects) on the right. In some cases, it is easier for students to write the effect first and then determine the cause.

Cause	Effect
Peter wages a war against Grandpa.	Hurt feelings (both Peter and Grandpa)
Peter wants to keep his room at all costs.	He makes choices he later regrets.

Literature
Using this organizer, students can see that a decision made by a story character—like Peter in *The War with Grandpa*—may lead to negative consequences.

Social Studies
Looking at a historical event as the "effect" helps students identify the cause (or causes). Working in small groups, students will often find a variety of causes for the same event. Then they can share and discuss why a particular event occurred in history.

Cause	Effect
Slavery—a moral issue—is questioned.	Laws to ban Slavery
Economic necessity for slave labor	The South fought to keep slaves and slavery.

Cause	Effect
Taking Drugs	
peer pressure	You do what you don't want to do.
educate (learn about drugs)	You know what drugs do to you.
refusal skills	You are prepared with ways to say, "No!"

General Classroom Use
Students need to see the connection between their behavior choices and the positive or negative effects of these choices. Have students examine a situation and discuss alternative choices. This activity allows them to see that making wise choices often yields positive results.

Name _____   Topic _____

Cause   ## Effect

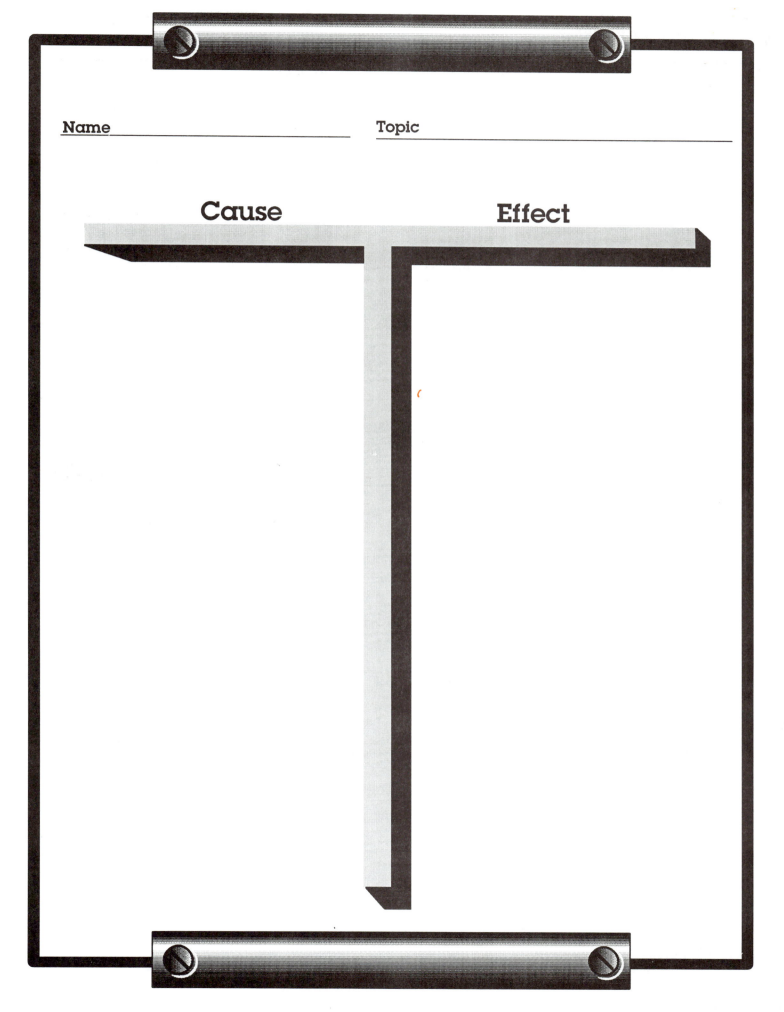

Identifying

PURPOSE Thinking ahead is an important skill in the decision-making process. The first step in research skills is to have students identify what they need to know. They must access their prior knowledge, then look for information to help them make a decision.

WHAT TO DO Students identify the problem, then write a plan to solve it. They support their thinking by gathering information from outside sources. Students show how they find the information, what they learn, and the conclusions they reach.

My problem is	Do foster children get treated like the Pinballs?
I think that	things have changed.
I'll find out by	calling the Dept. of Social Services and ask.
I found out that	it is amazing, but it can still happen today.
Conclusions	Things should be better for foster children.

Literature
While reading a good story, students often want or need to know more about a particular topic. Stating this as a problem question helps students find the answers. For example, after reading *The Pinballs* by Byars, students might find out about foster care—is it like the description in the book?

Science
Use this graphic organizer to plan a science activity and reinforce questioning, predicting, and research skills. For example, when planting a tree, students pose their question (problem) and list where they will look for the answer. Then they write what they find out and what they need to do.

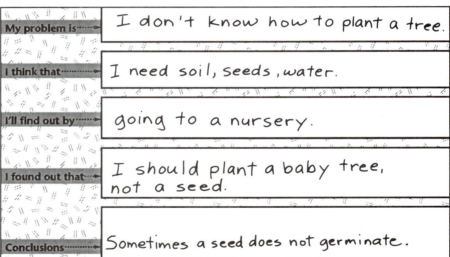

My problem is	I don't know how to plant a tree.
I think that	I need soil, seeds, water.
I'll find out by	going to a nursery.
I found out that	I should plant a baby tree, not a seed.
Conclusions	Sometimes a seed does not germinate.

My problem is	I need to learn about birds.
I think that	I'll go to the library.
I'll find out by	looking in the card catalogue, asking the librarian.
I found out that	there are lots of bird books and magazines.
Conclusions	I'm glad I asked for help. The librarian was helpful.

✎ General Classroom Use
When they research a topic, students should formulate a plan to find answers to their questions. Students use the organizer to clearly state the problem and they make their "best guess" as to where they will find solutions. Doing this, students can test or think through their ideas ahead of time.

Name _____

Title/Topic _____

DECIDING

My problem is········▶

I think that ··········▶

I'll find out by ······▶

I found out that ·······▶

Conclusions ·········▶

Identifying

PURPOSE This organizer helps students understand the decision-making process. Students are challenged to identify a question, select possible options, look at the pros and cons of each option, then come to a decision.

WHAT TO DO Students determine a question they want answered. They brainstorm choices and options, providing opportunities to expand their thinking. They write their first, second, and third choices, and the reasons for their selection.

Literature
Characters, like Jonas in *The Giver* by Lowry, often make decisions that affect the outcome of the story. Have students use this organizer to evaluate a character's decisions.

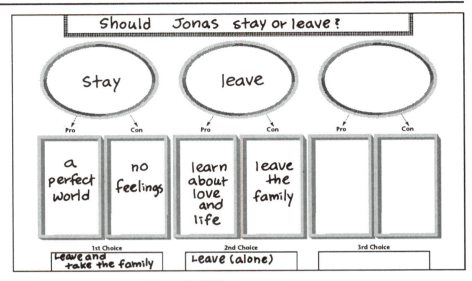

Should Jonas stay or leave?

Stay		leave			
Pro	Con	Pro	Con	Pro	Con
a perfect world	no feelings	learn about love and life	leave the family		

1st Choice: Leave and take the family
2nd Choice: Leave (alone)
3rd Choice:

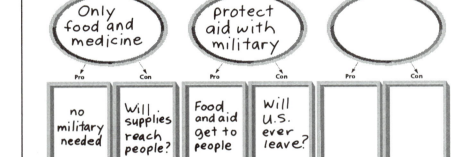

Should the U.S. help Somalia?

Only food and medicine		protect aid with military			
Pro	Con	Pro	Con	Pro	Con
no military needed	Will supplies reach people?	Food and aid get to people	Will U.S. ever leave?		

1st Choice: protect with military
2nd Choice: medicine and food only
3rd Choice:

Social Studies
Looking at the pros and cons of a political situation helps students become aware of how difficult it is to make a good decision—for example, when our leaders decide to involve the country in the problems of another land.

General Classroom Use
When a classroom problem arises, have students examine possible solutions by using the Choices organizer.

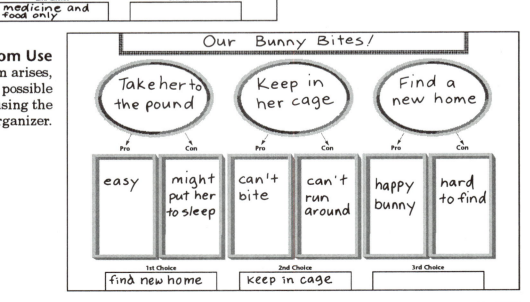

Our Bunny Bites!

Take her to the pound		Keep in her cage		Find a new home	
Pro	Con	Pro	Con	Pro	Con
easy	might put her to sleep	can't bite	can't run around	happy bunny	hard to find

1st Choice: find new home
2nd Choice: keep in cage
3rd Choice:

Choices

Name _____

Title/Topic _____

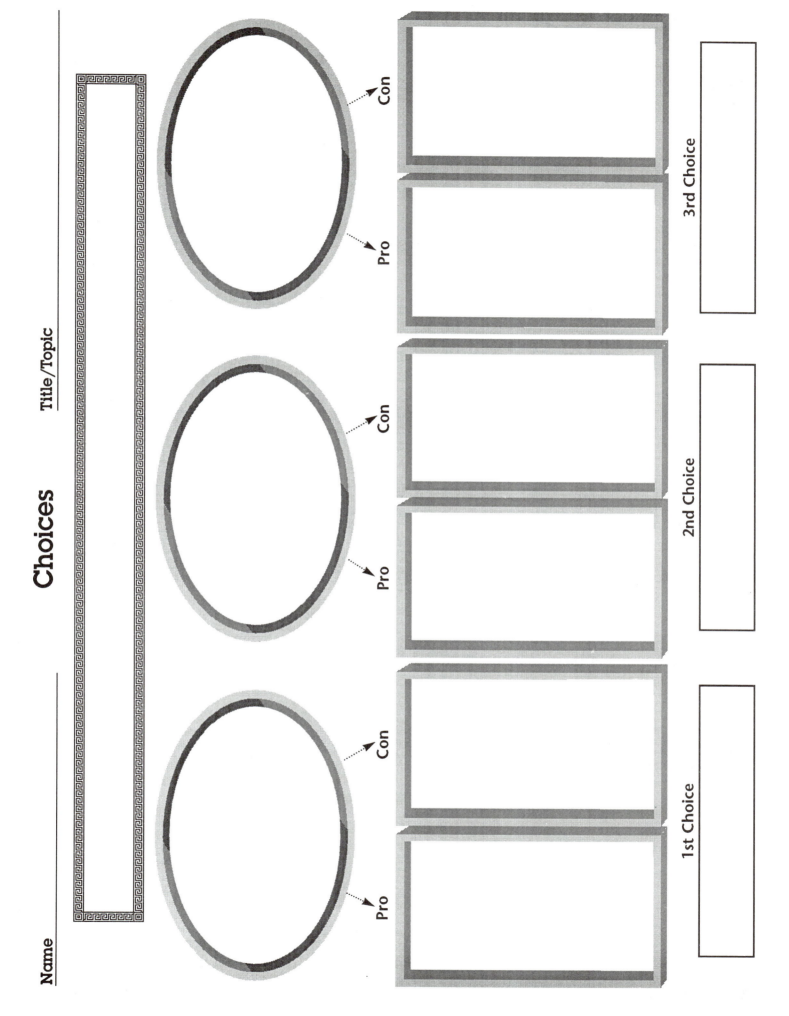

Pro

Con

Pro

Con

Pro

Con

1st Choice _____

2nd Choice _____

3rd Choice _____

Creating

PURPOSE In this organizer students identify special or meaningful words and phrases from a text. Place these around the room for future reference or have students keep them in a notebook to use in their writing and oral reports.

WHAT TO DO Write the title or name of the topic in the center of the flower. Students work individually or in a group to identify words or phrases for each petal. The words may relate to the topic or may be special phrases the student wants to remember.

 Literature
Students may write the topic or the book title in the flower center and the author's name on the stem. As students read, they look for phrases that tell about something specific—for example, the story problem—or for descriptive words. They write these on the petals. Encourage students to add more flower petals if needed.

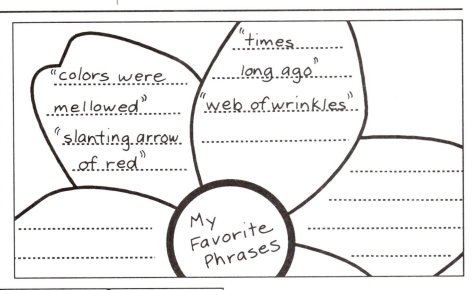

 Geography
Students look through a book for phrases that describe a specific location. For example, when studying an area, ask students to write words and phrases clarifying geographical characteristics.

✏ **General Classroom Use**
Discuss the month's weather with the class, then have students gather special words or phrases from their reading to use in a class book or journal.

Blooming Words and Phrases

Creating

PURPOSE Learning to plan is a lifelong skill. When students plan ahead, they increase their likelihood of success and have time for revisions and improvement. The Building Plan helps students with organizational skills and study habits.

WHAT TO DO Students write what they need to complete a project. They may predict outcomes or record what actually happens. Students evaluate their plan after completing the project and revise their predictions if necessary.

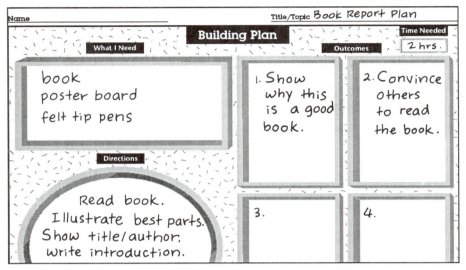

Literature

Individually or in groups, students use the Building Plan to help organize and plan a report or project based on a special book.

Science

Ask science groups to write a Building Plan for their project. Appoint a student committee to use this plan to evaluate the group's outcomes. The committee checks off the outcomes as they are completed.

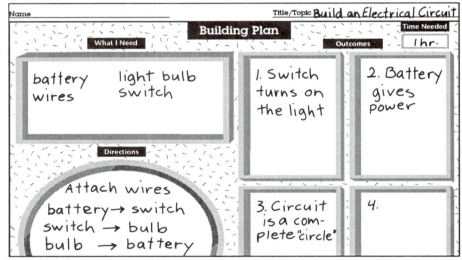

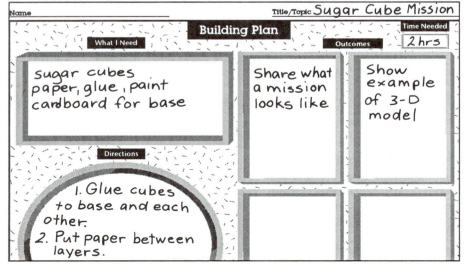

General Classroom Use

When students have a class project, they can use this organizer to help them prepare. Students should spend the greatest amount of time developing the materials and directions sections of their Building Plan.

Name

Title/Topic

Building Plan

Time Needed

Outcomes

What I Need

Directions

Recording

PURPOSE A good report includes the five Ws—Who, What, When, Where, and Why. In this organizer students find and record information for each category. This helps students recall information and encourages them to look for these elements in all reporting tasks.

WHAT TO DO As they research, students search for and write specific information for each of the five Ws. They use the categories in any order when they compile their information into written or oral form.

Literature

Gathering information from a story like *Mufaro's Beautiful Daughters* by Steptoe is similar to gathering information for a report. After they organize their thoughts, students may use the separate information areas to write paragraphs.

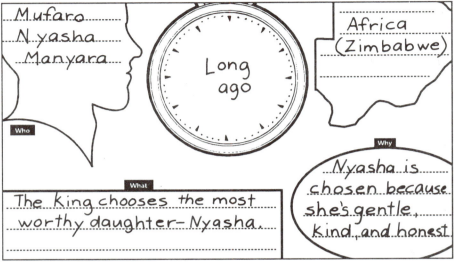

Who: Mufaro, Nyasha, Manyara

When: Long ago

Where: Africa (Zimbabwe)

What: The king chooses the most worthy daughter—Nyasha.

Why: Nyasha is chosen because she's gentle, kind, and honest.

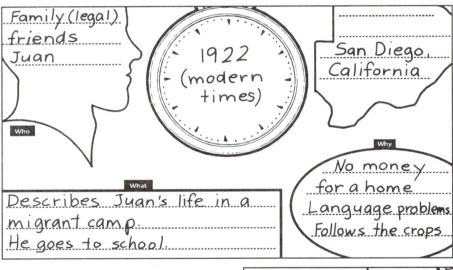

Who: Family (legal), friends, Juan

When: 1922 (modern times)

Where: San Diego, California

What: Describes Juan's life in a migrant camp. He goes to school.

Why: No money for a home. Language problems. Follows the crops.

Social Studies

Students use the chart to organize information from a nonfiction book like *A Migrant Family* by Brimner. As students learn about the difficult life of migrant workers, they use the Five Ws chart to record details for a writing assignment.

General Classroom Use

Use the organizer to help students share information about classroom events. Encourage students to compile the information into a classroom newspaper or class book.

Who: Floppy, our bunny

When: May 15 (during the night)

Where: In her cage at school

What: Floppy had 3 babies.

Why: She was pregnant (expecting babies.)

The Five Ws

Where

Why

When

What

Who

Recording

PURPOSE Students make better predictions or guesses when they examine the possible outcomes of their actions. Students improve their planning and their understanding of consequences as they make and evaluate their predictions.

WHAT TO DO First students list what they know about the topic. Then they use this information to write predictions or guesses (options). For each prediction they write what might happen (results), evaluate the choices, determine the best, and reflect on their predictions.

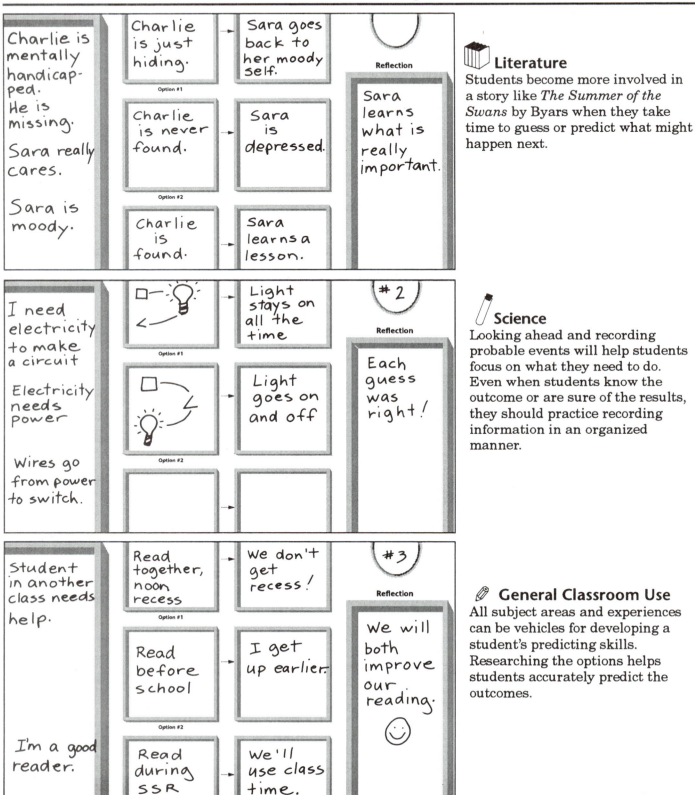

Literature
Students become more involved in a story like *The Summer of the Swans* by Byars when they take time to guess or predict what might happen next.

Science
Looking ahead and recording probable events will help students focus on what they need to do. Even when students know the outcome or are sure of the results, they should practice recording information in an organized manner.

General Classroom Use
All subject areas and experiences can be vehicles for developing a student's predicting skills. Researching the options helps students accurately predict the outcomes.

My Best Guess by _____

Title/Topic _____

Best Choice

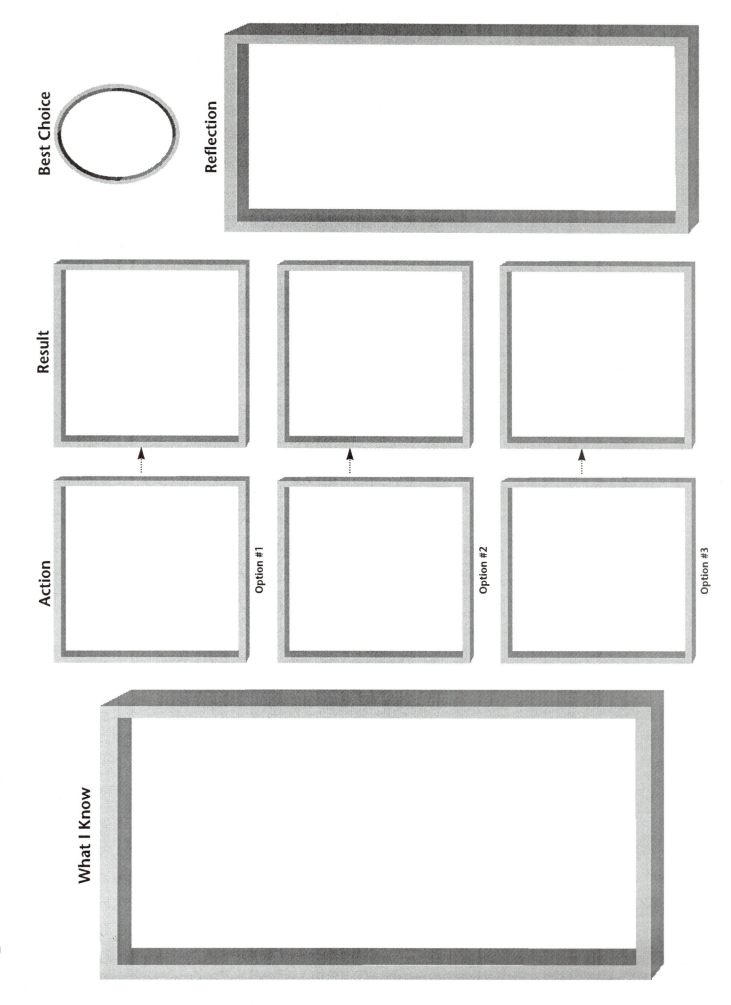

Reflection

Result

Action

Option #1

Option #2

Option #3

What I Know

Recording

PURPOSE Determining the focus is a skill students will use throughout their lives. In the Learning Record there are prompts to help students organize the information they find.

WHAT TO DO Students list what they already know about the topic. Based on their discussion they determine what they want to find out. (This gives them a clear direction for their research.) Students then list the resources they might use to find the information.

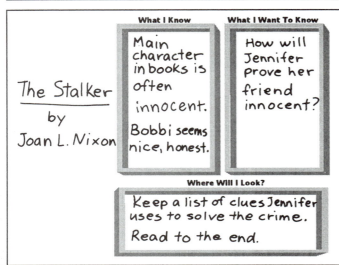

The Stalker
by
Joan L. Nixon

What I Know
Main character in books is often innocent.
Bobbi seems nice, honest.

What I Want To Know
How will Jennifer prove her friend innocent?

Where Will I Look?
Keep a list of clues Jennifer uses to solve the crime.
Read to the end.

 Literature
As students read a book like *The Stalker* by Nixon, they use the Learning Record to reflect on their reading. Completing the "What I Want to Know" box helps students focus their future reading as they search for answers to their questions.

Science
Have students select report topics that interest them. To help them access their prior knowledge, ask students to list what they already know about the subject and what they want to learn. For example, in a study of spiders, students can organize their learning and focus their research by listing specific questions.

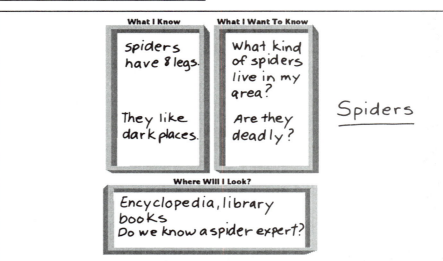

What I Know
spiders have 8 legs.
They like dark places.

What I Want To Know
What kind of spiders live in my area?
Are they deadly?

Spiders

Where Will I Look?
Encyclopedia, library books
Do we know a spider expert?

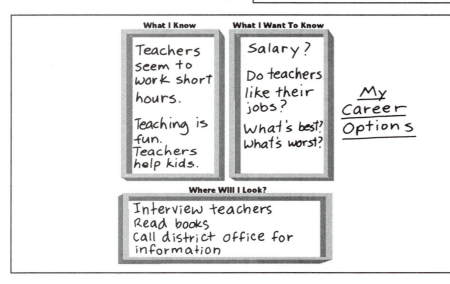

What I Know
Teachers seem to work short hours.
Teaching is fun. Teachers help kids.

What I Want To Know
Salary?
Do teachers like their jobs?
What's best? What's worst?

My Career Options

Where Will I Look?
Interview teachers
Read books
Call district office for information

General Classroom Use
Use the chart to help students research personal issues such as career options. Encourage them to include interviews and surveys as they gather information.

_____'s Learning Record

Title/Topic _____

What I Know

What I Want to Know

Where Will I Look?

Recording

PURPOSE This is an easy way to organize information for an oral or written report. The Data Boxes allow students to visualize each component of their report.

WHAT TO DO In the introduction students "set the stage" for their topic. In each body box they write one topic area followed by informational details. Help students select the three main points through teacher modeling and class discussions.

Literature

Use the Data Boxes to organize information for a book report. For example, students determine three main points they want to share from a favorite book like *Flossie and the Fox* by McKissack. These then become three separate paragraphs in their report.

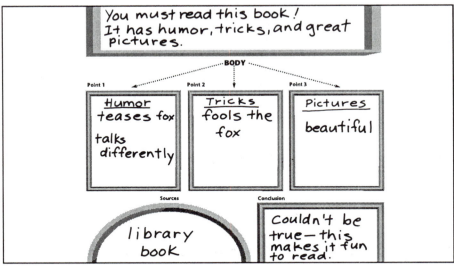

Social Studies

This organizer helps students focus on their topic's main points. Students research information and add details to each identified main point. In the example students have organized their research during a study of famous artists.

General Classroom Use

Have students use this organizer to record information they gather about their classmates' habits. For example, students interview one another, organize the collected information into categories, and share it.

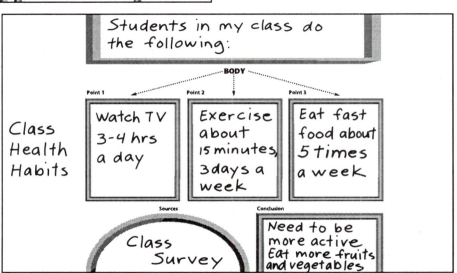

Data Boxes

Introduction

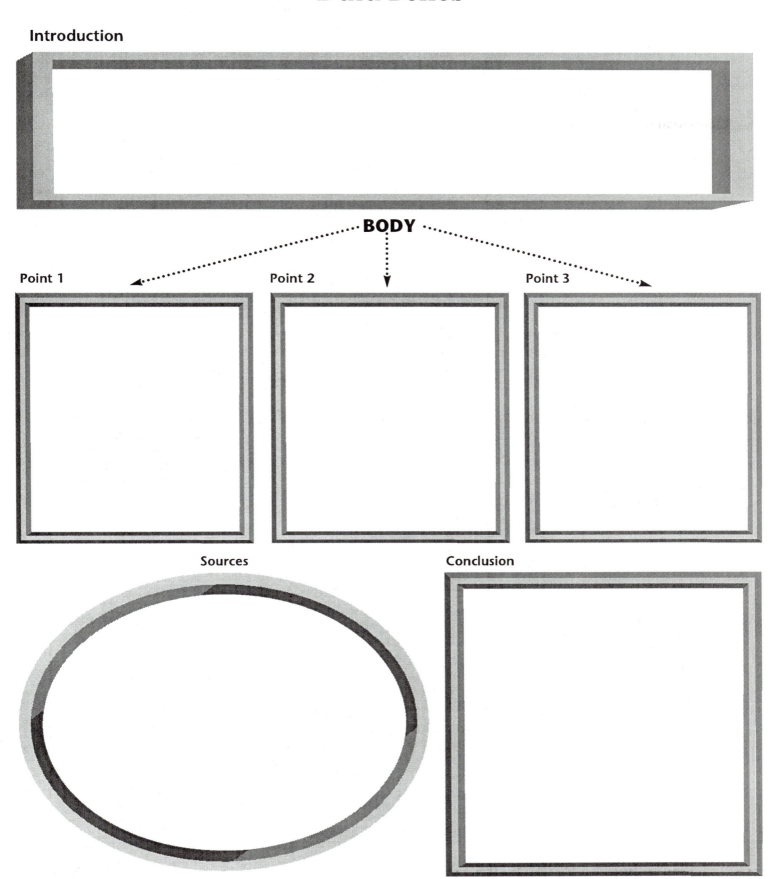

Recording

PURPOSE This Research Organizer helps students think about, organize, and record the information they collect for a project or report.

WHAT TO DO Students record data and information from all the resources they use. Then they write their conclusion(s). Students may wish to use one chart for each resource or reference book they consult.

 **Literature**
Historical fiction like *Roll of Thunder, Hear My Cry* by Taylor helps students understand a specific time period. As students read the book they record information which they can later check in reference books.

> Title _Roll of Thunder, Hear My Cry_
> Source(s) _class library book_
>
> Information I learned:
> 1. _In this book —_
>   _Black people had to take a different bus._
> 2. _Black and white children went to different schools._
> 3. _Blacks got secondhand textbooks._
>
> Conclusions _Racial issues have changed, but we still need to work on this._

> Title _Spiders_
> Source(s) _"S" encyclopedia, World Book, 1993_
>
> Information I learned:
> 1. _Spiders have 8 legs and often live in dark places_
> 2. _Most spiders are not harmful. They help by eating insects_
> 3. _Male spiders are often prettier_
>
> Conclusions _I shouldn't be afraid of spiders. They are more helpful than harmful_

Science
Use this organizer as a follow-up to the Learning Record (pages 38-39). For example, after students identify what they want to know about spiders on the Learning Record, they record their information on the Research Organizer.

General Classroom Use
Sometimes classroom problems need to be researched. For example, when the classroom cockatiel won't talk, assign students to find out why. List the information, then have students discuss their conclusions.

> Title _Birds Can Talk_
> Source(s) _Birds U.S.A. Volume 4, No. 1, 1992-93_
>
> Information I learned:
> 1. _Choose a male bird._
> 2. _Don't put a mirror in the cage._
> 3. _Teach one word at a time. Repeat it._
>
> Conclusions _It may be difficult for our class bird to talk!_

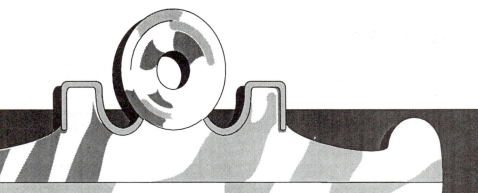

—————————'s Research Organizer

Title --

Source(s)--

Information I learned:

1.--

2.--

3.--

4.--

Conclusion(s)--

Mapping

PURPOSE All stories have common elements—setting, characters, problem, and solution. The Sentence Map provides an easy way for students to identify these story elements as they write the sentence endings.

WHAT TO DO Model the organizer with the whole class as students complete the sentences with information from their text or other resources. Students may choose to follow one main character through the entire story.

 **Literature**

Groups or individuals use information from a book like *Ming Lo Moves the Mountain* by Lobel to complete their sentences. If students have different sentence endings, they should compare and discuss them.

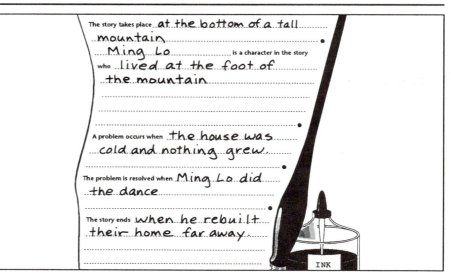

The story takes place **at the bottom of a tall mountain**
Ming Lo is a character in the story who **lived at the foot of the mountain**

A problem occurs when **the house was cold and nothing grew**

The problem is resolved when **Ming Lo did the dance**

The story ends **when he rebuilt their home far away**

The story takes place **at the San Diego Zoo**
Gordy is a character in the story who **grows up in the zoo nursery**

A problem occurs when **Gordy needs to go to the wild animal park**
The problem is resolved when **Gordy learns to get along with other animals**
The story ends **Gordy joins another gorilla**

Science

When they study a historical figure in social studies or an animal in science, students can increase their understanding by reading a nonfiction book. For example, in *Gordy Gorilla* by Irvine, students learn that gorillas have characteristics similar to humans.

General Classroom Use

By viewing classroom events as parts of a story, students discover they can record these in a story form. For example, when the classroom snake gets out of its cage, students may record the event by telling or writing about it in a class book or newspaper.

The story takes place **in Room P-2, Golden Hill School**
Bobby the snake is a character in the story who **lives in a cage in the room**

A problem occurs when **Bobby escapes**

The problem is resolved when **the principal finds him in her desk**

The story ends **When the snake is returned by a scared principal**

Sentence Map

Title ....

by ....

The story takes place ....

.... •

.... is a character in the story

who ....

....

....

....

.... •

A problem occurs when ....

....

.... •

The problem is resolved when ....

....

.... •

The story ends ....

....

....

.... •

INK

Mapping

PURPOSE This simple mapping activity helps students understand the importance of a character. They identify the character's goals and problems and determine how he or she reaches the goal or solves the problem.

WHAT TO DO Students choose someone from a book or real life and use the Story Pattern to record the character's desires or motives. Then they follow the character and record what happens.

 Literature
Use the organizer for a beginning story mapping activity for the whole class. Students—in groups or individually—select one character (for example, Peter in *The War with Grandpa* by Smith) and complete the Story Pattern. Encourage students to choose different characters and compare their answers.

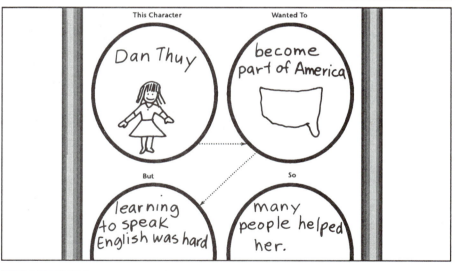

 Social Studies
As students complete the Story Pattern for a character in a nonfiction book like *Dan Thuy's New Life in America* by O'Connor, they begin to understand the individual motives and the life stories that make up our country's history.

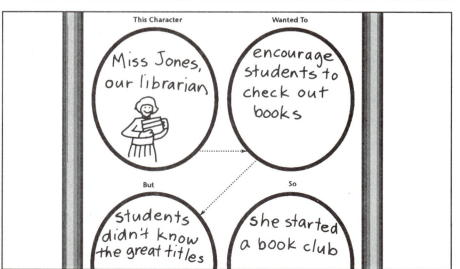

✎ **General Classroom Use**
Use the Story Pattern to help organize classroom events, then compile them into a class book or yearly journal. For example, ask students to collect an information page about each special person who works in the school.

Name _____   Title _____

Story Pattern

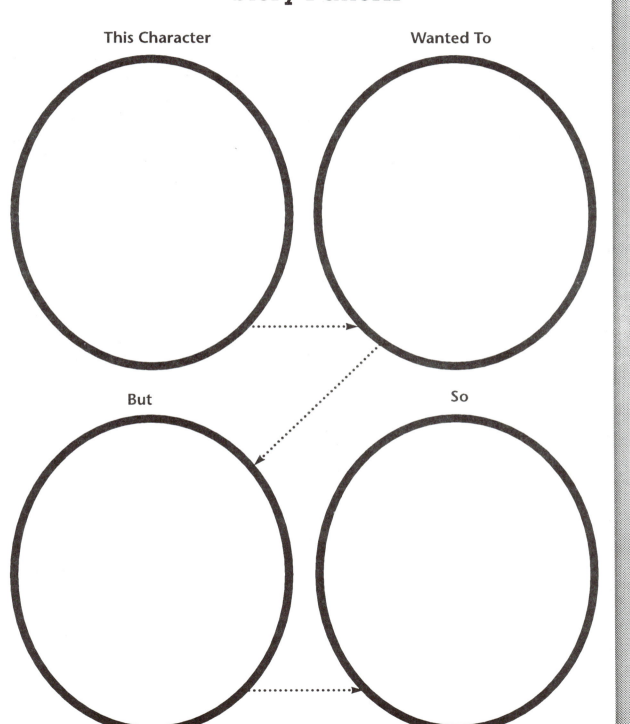

This Character

Wanted To

But

So

Comparing

PURPOSE Comparing events that happened long ago with contemporary events helps students see changes that occur over time. For example, looking at how things were done in the past may help students appreciate the present.

WHAT TO DO On the left side students record information or events from the past. On the right they record parallel information. In order to make accurate comparisons, students should write one "Now" statement for each "Then" statement.

Then

wood house

water from the creek

broom to sweep

all grades in one room

Now

variety of materials

water from the faucet

vacuum

classes divided by grade

Literature

After students read a book about life long ago—for example, *Little House in the Big Woods* by Wilder—they record information on the organizer. They may also identify how a character's life would be different today than it was in the book.

Social Studies

History comes alive when students compare their lives with those of long ago. For example, students research how people made a living long ago and compare it with occupations today. Or they may contrast the transportation, politics, and events of a time past with those of today.

Then

Jamestown, 1600s

log fires

hand-built homes

grow or kill your own food

Now

Jamestown, 1900s

gas heat

housing developments

get food from the store

Then   4th Grade   Now

September

handwritten reports

calculate only with paper and pencil

May

type on a computer

can use a calculator

General Classroom Use

Use the chart as an assessment tool to determine what students have learned at the end of a unit of study. Or at the end of the school year, have students compare what they know now with what they knew in September.

Name _____   Title/Topic _____

Then   **Now**

Comparing

PURPOSE This is a challenging organizer that elicits higher level thinking and allows students to identify complicated relationships. As students record the attributes of objects or events, they make judgments about their similarities, differences, and relationships.

WHAT TO DO Familiarize students with the double Venn before they compare three objects or events. Students decide which attributes are shared by only two and which by all three. They write similarities inside the overlapping sections and differences on the outside of each circle.

Literature

Students use the Triple Venn to compare three versions of the same story, for example, *Jack and the Beanstalk* by Cauley, *Jim and the Beanstalk* by Briggs, and *Jack and the Bean Tree* by Haley. In the overlapping portions, they record parts that are the same. In the outer portions, they record differences specific to each story. Students may also compare three characters in similar roles or three story endings.

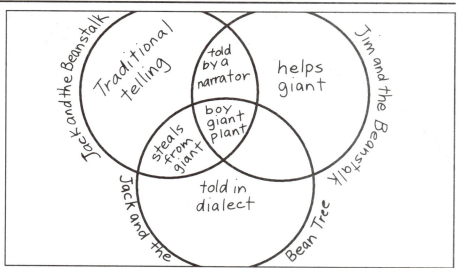

Music

Have students listen to three musical selections and diagram them according to tempo, instruments heard, and type of music (for example, folk, classical, and contemporary).

General Classroom Use

Have students compare three group or classroom projects on the same topic. This activity gives students the opportunity to learn from one another, experience different viewpoints, and gain insight into others' thinking.

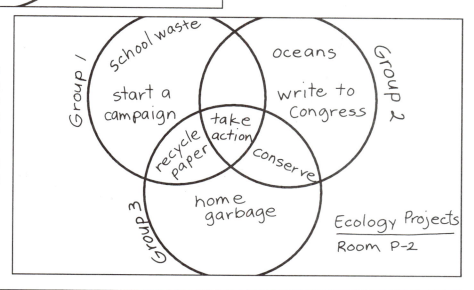

Name _____   Title/Topic _____

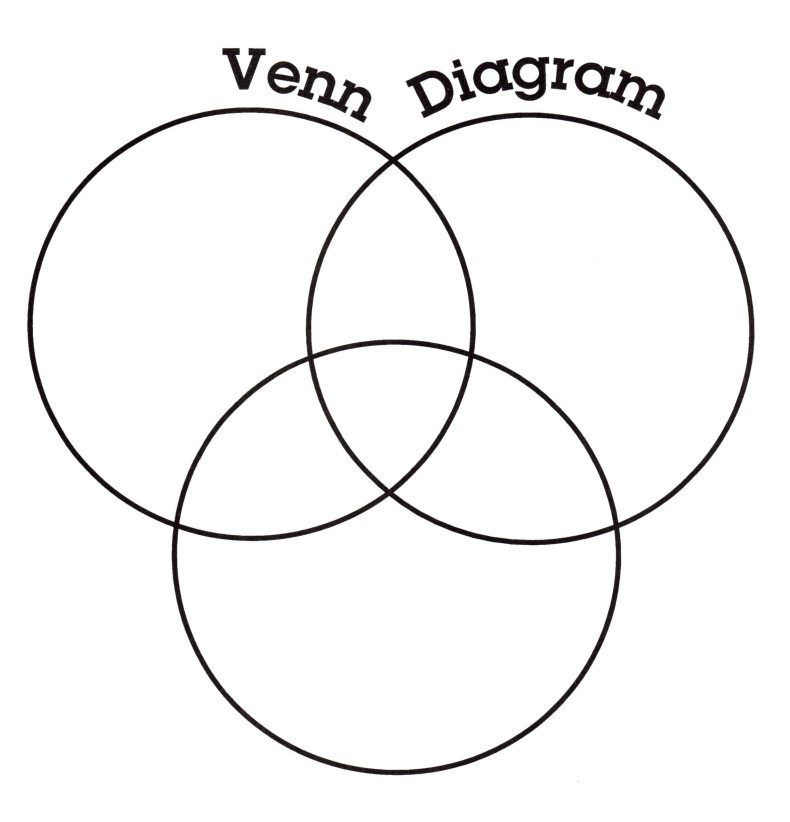

Evaluating

PURPOSE Use this organizer to explore point of view. Have students place themselves into a story or event and predict the thoughts or feelings of a character. Students then use this information as a springboard for their writing.

WHAT TO DO Write the person's name and the situation or event under consideration. Inside the head, students draw or write what the character is thinking and feeling at that moment.

Literature

As a prompt for this activity, use a quotation or a specific event from a story like *Jack and the Beanstalk* by Cauley. Students work individually or in partners to depict what the character is thinking at the time of the quotation.

Social Studies

Students explore a current or historical event by investigating the thoughts of a principal character. This is a good opportunity to discuss point of view as individuals or groups may see the character's view of the event somewhat differently.

General Classroom Use

Class members may react to a new or difficult event in a variety of ways. Have students complete a Mind Look and share their reactions. This process helps students clarify their thoughts and feelings and promotes acceptance of others' viewpoints.

Students may also share information about themselves— their likes and dislikes.

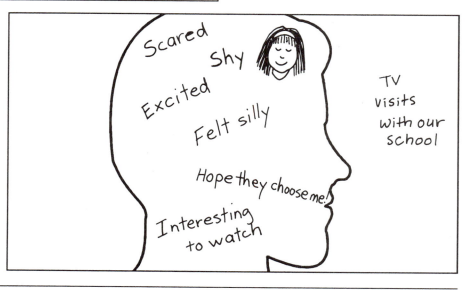

Mind Look for _____

Name _____

Evaluating

PURPOSE When students give a fictional—or real-life—character a Report Card grade, they must make some evaluative decisions. The process of determining the qualities to evaluate is as beneficial for students as the actual evaluation.

WHAT TO DO Students determine the qualities they will evaluate. (Older students should select evaluation areas that show more depth of character.) They place a letter grade or check mark in the appropriate circle, adding a comment to explain the rating.

Report Card for _The Wolf (3 Little Pigs)_
Written by _Raquel_

Traits/Characteristics Evaluated	1	2	3	4	5
Goodness	good ◯	◯	◯	◯	bad ⊗

The wolf ate the pigs!

	1	2	3	4	5
Luck	lucky ◯	◯	◯	⊗	unlucky ◯

He got caught.

Report Card for _Abraham Lincoln_
Written by _Cathy_

Traits/Characteristics Evaluated	1	2	3	4	5
Honesty	Ⓐ	◯	◯	◯	◯

He was known as "Honest Abe."

	1	2	3	4	5
Peacekeeper	◯	◯	◯	Ⓓ	◯

The nation went to war.

Report Card for _Our Class Fire Drill_
Written by _Dan's group_

Traits/Characteristics Evaluated	1	2	3	4	5
Noise level	very quiet ◯	⊗	◯	◯	loud ◯

We remembered to walk quietly.

	1	2	3	4	5
Speed	fast ◯	◯	⊗	◯	slow ◯

We still need to practice.

Literature
Ask students to evaluate a story character—for example, the wolf in *The Three Little Pigs*. They work in small groups to arrive at a consensus on the grades, then give reasons to justify their thinking.

Social Studies
Historical figures make great Report Card subjects! For example, when evaluating Abraham Lincoln, students might give him a high grade for honesty and dedication to human rights; and a low grade as a peacekeeper. Students then write why they gave Lincoln the grades.

General Classroom Use
Have students evaluate a current event or classroom activity. For example, after evaluating a class fire drill, discuss how the class can improve their "grade." Students might also use the Report Card to grade their home fire drills.

Report Card for _____

Written by _____

Traits/Characteristics Evaluated	1	2	3	4	5
----------------------- -----------------------	◯	◯	◯	◯	◯
----------------------- -----------------------	◯	◯	◯	◯	◯
----------------------- -----------------------	◯	◯	◯	◯	◯
----------------------- -----------------------	◯	◯	◯	◯	◯
----------------------- -----------------------	◯	◯	◯	◯	◯

Comments _____

_____

_____

Evaluating

PURPOSE As part of our learning experience, we need to be able to evaluate our strengths and weaknesses. Taking a "Look At Me" gives students the opportunity to reflect on a person's qualities and accomplishments.

WHAT TO DO Students write activities that are easy or difficult for a character. They look at what the character has accomplished, then project into the future what the character wants to know or learn. Students may want to create a new box or leave one blank.

Literature

Story characters, like Grace in *Amazing Grace* by Mary Hoffman, usually have traits that make them interesting to the reader. Students use the organizer to collect information about the character and evaluate his or her actions.

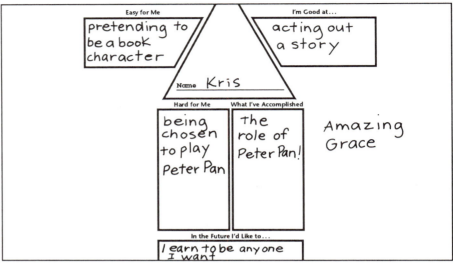

Social Studies

Have students evaluate a historical character or well-known person in the news. This is an excellent activity to extend through classroom discussion and writing.

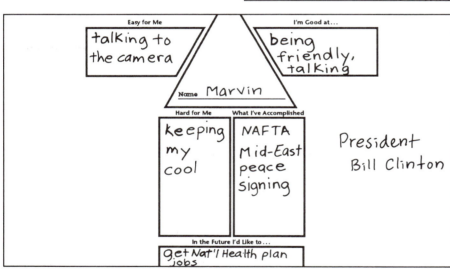

General Classroom Use

Ask students to evaluate their strengths and weaknesses in the classroom. Have students complete a Look At Me organizer at the beginning and end of the year—and point out their growth! Place a copy of both pages in the student's portfolio.

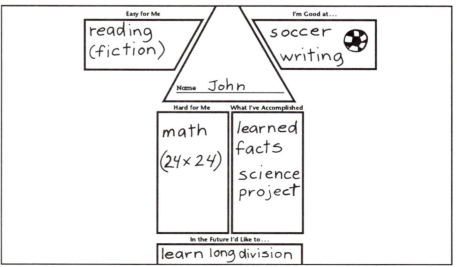

Creative Teaching Press

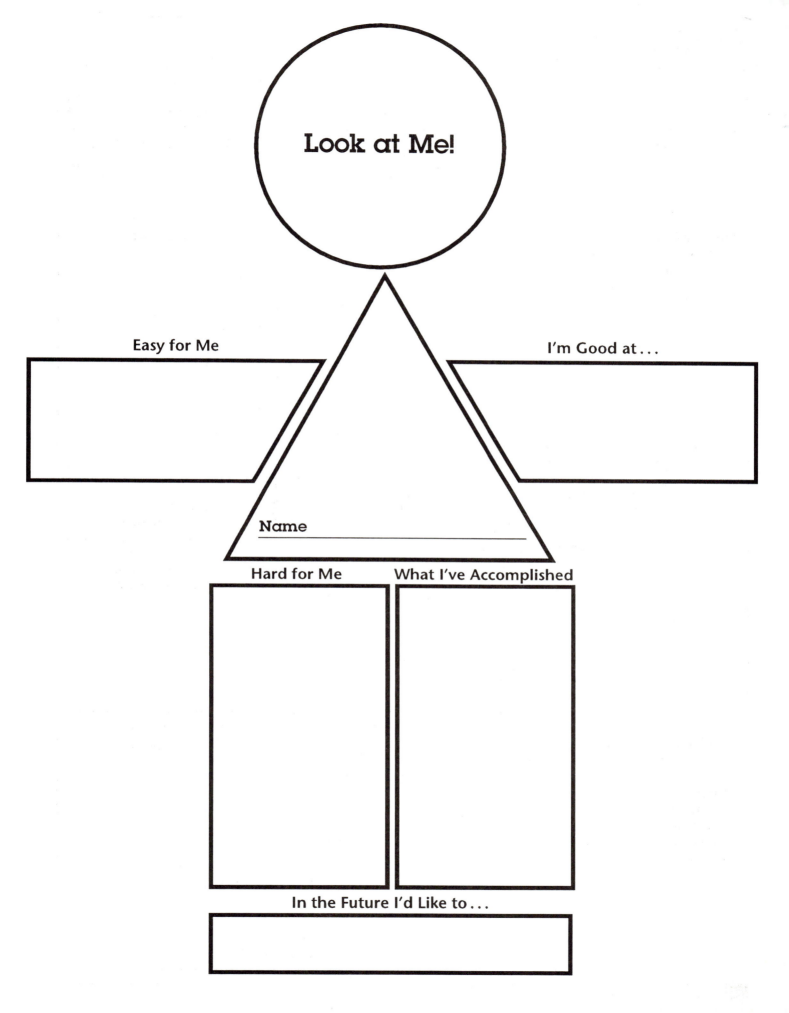

Look at Me!

Easy for Me

I'm Good at . . .

Name

Hard for Me

What I've Accomplished

In the Future I'd Like to . . .

Evaluating

PURPOSE This Triple Entry Journal helps students relate their own experiences to a text. In their response, students are asked to make personal connections to the subject, thus expanding their understanding of the "big picture."

WHAT TO DO Students should be familiar with a double entry journal before attempting this organizer. Students copy a meaningful quotation and write their thoughts and feelings about it. Finally, they relate what they learned to the world in general.

Quotes	Thoughts and Feelings	Relating
There's only one thing to do at a time like this — bake a cake. p. 34	My Mom gave us cookies when we were sad	Is this why people eat when they're depressed?
	Ira looks sad. I was sad when my friend moved	Moving is good and bad.

 Literature
Many picture books, for example, *Ira Says Goodbye* by Waber, have meaningful text for all students. Ask students to respond to the pictures as well as the text in the book.

Quotes	Thoughts and Feelings	Relating
Grandpa won't know who I am.	When I see names on graves, the people don't seem real	So many people die in wars.
I'd rather have him here.	Remembering isn't always enough.	How can we prevent wars like that one?

 Social Studies
Students use the organizer to relate a fictional text to historical events or characters. For example, in *The Wall* Eve Bunting expresses the feelings of people affected by the war. As students respond to the story, they become aware of people's pain and the need to work toward world peace.

Quotes	Thoughts and Feelings	Relating
My	Museum Field	Trip
I'll see old things.	Things used long ago were primitive!	We have it easier nowadays.
I hate pictures and art.	It wasn't so boring. I saw interesting stuff	I'd go again! I shouldn't prejudge.

✏ **General Classroom Use**
The Triple Entry Journal becomes a valuable reflective tool when students evaluate a classroom experience. Students write the event—or a quotation—in the first column. They write their reactions to the event and then look at it from a broader perspective. This is a great pre-writing activity for class journals or books.

Triple Entry Journal

Quotes	Thoughts and Feelings	Relating

Evaluating

PURPOSE In this organizer students use higher level thinking skills as they analyze different viewpoints and determine how these affect a person's actions and reactions.

WHAT TO DO Students record each character's perspective and the impact or results of their thinking. Finally, students write their thoughts, questions, or observations about the situation, making connections to their lives.

View Points of:	Thoughts/Feelings	Impact	Reflections
Dad + Mom	Want Gpa to come Make him welcome	unaware of what's happening	If my G'pa came to live with me, I wouldn't want to give up my room.
Peter	unfair wants to keep his room.	writes nasty notes to G'pa	
G'pa Jack	depressed about moving	mopes but wants to get along with Peter	

Literature

Students analyze how each character from a story like *The War with Grandpa* by Smith feels or thinks about a particular event. Based on this perspective, students record what action the character takes and the results of that action.

Social Studies

Students choose a historical event—for example, the Revolutionary War—and analyze the principal characters' thoughts and emotions. They record how these ideas affected the event and reflect on what "could have been."

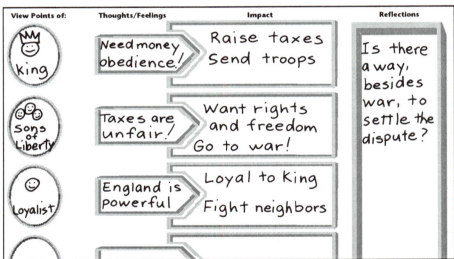

View Points of:	Thoughts/Feelings	Impact	Reflections
king	Need money obedience!	Raise taxes Send troops	Is there a way, besides war, to settle the dispute?
Sons of Liberty	Taxes are unfair!	Want rights and freedom Go to war!	
Loyalist	England is powerful	Loyal to King Fight neighbors	

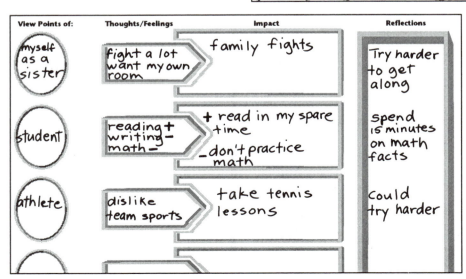

View Points of:	Thoughts/Feelings	Impact	Reflections
myself as a sister	fight a lot want my own room	family fights	Try harder to get along
student	reading + writing + math -	+ read in my spare time - don't practice math	spend 15 minutes on math facts
athlete	dislike team sports	take tennis lessons	Could try harder

General Classroom Use

Students can use the chart to analyze their roles in life. Encourage them to set goals for growth and change.

Different Perspectives

Name _____

Title/Topic _____

Reflections

Impact

Thoughts/Feelings

View Points of:

Bibliography

Amazing Grace
Mary Hoffman
(Scholastic, 1991)

Annie and the Old One
Miska Miles (Atlantic/Little
Brown, 1971)

"Birds Can Talk"
Karyn New (Birds USA 1992-
93, p.60)

*Dan Thuy's New Life in
America*
Karen O'Conner (Lerner, 1992)

Flossie and the Fox
Patricia McKissack (Dial, 1986)

The Giver
Lois Lowry
(Houghton Mifflin, 1993)

Gordy Gorilla
Georgeanne Irvine (Simon &
Schuster, 1990)

I Know an Old Lady
Nadine Westcott
(Atlantic/Little Brown, 1980)

If You Give a Mouse a Cookie
Laura Numeroff (Harper, 1986)

Ira Says Goodbye
Bernard Waber
(Houghton Mifflin, 1988)

Jack and the Beanstalk
Lorinda Cauley (Putnam, 1983)

Jack and the Bean Tree
Gail Haley (Crown, 1986)

Jim and the Beanstalk
Raymond Briggs
(Coward, 1970)

Little House in the Big Woods
Laura Ingalls Wilder
(Harper, 1953)

A Migrant Family
Larry Dane Brimner
(Lerner, 1992)

Ming Lo Moves the Mountain
Arnold Lobel (Morrow, 1982)

Miss Rumphius
Barbara Cooney (Viking, 1982)

Mufaro's Beautiful Daughters
John Steptoe (Lothrop, 1987)

Owl Moon
Jane Yolen (Philomel, 1987)

The Pinballs
Betsy Byars (Harper, 1977)

Roll of Thunder, Hear My Cry
Mildred Taylor (Dial, 1976)

The Stalker
Joan Lowery Nixon (Dell, 1985)

The Summer of the Swans
Betsy Byars (Viking, 1970)

The Three Little Pigs
James Marshall (Dial, 1989)

Thunder Cake
Patricia Polacco
(Philomel, 1990)

The Twenty-one Balloons
William Pené du Bois
(Viking, 1947)

The Wall
Eve Bunting (Clarion, 1990)

The War with Grandpa
Robert Smith (Delacorte, 1984)

Your Own Organizer

PURPOSE Combine, adapt, or create a new organizer in order to meet your special needs or for a specific task.

WHAT TO DO Encourage students to develop combinations and variations of the graphic organizers. They should determine the purpose of their organizer and consider the complexity of the text.

 Literature

Combine the Problem–Solution chart (page 22) with Deciding (page 26). Using students' suggested solutions to Miss Rumphius' problems, write a plan to implement one solution.

Solution

She planted lupines

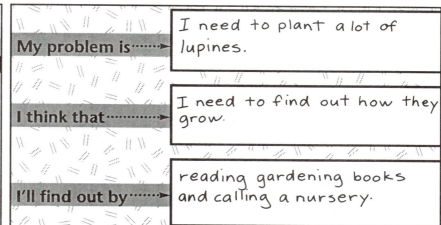

My problem is······▶ I need to plant a lot of lupines.

I think that············▶ I need to find out how they grow.

I'll find out by·······▶ reading gardening books and calling a nursery.

 Social Studies

Help students organize information from their textbook. They can use four shapes, writing each piece of information on a separate shape.

Students write chapter headings (main ideas) on the predominant shape and second-level information (subheadings) on the next shape.

They read the information under each subheading, identify the important details, and write these on the third shape.

For the fourth shape, they write a summary.

Have students cut out the shapes and attach a magnetic backing. They can arrange the information on a magnetic board and move the shapes around, linking the related. Rearrangement is easy.

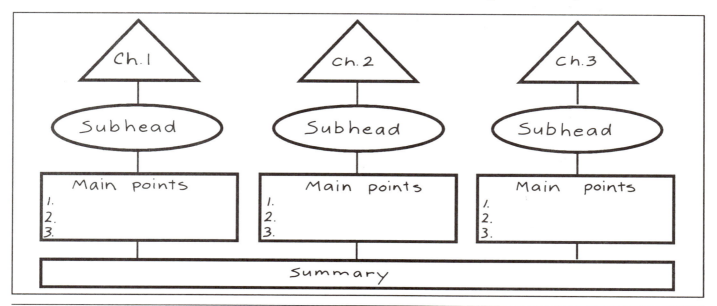